Use short vowel rhyming families to make new words.

at	**ed**	**ing**	**ock**	**ug**
b a t	b_____	k_____	cl_____	b_____
c_____	f_____	r_____	d_____	d_____
f_____	l_____	s_____	l_____	h_____
h_____	r_____	sw_____	s_____	r_____
s_____	sl_____	w_____	r_____	t_____

Use your new words to make up a silly story. Read your story.
Answers may vary.

One day a _____ went on a trip. He packed

a _____ , a _____ , a _____ ,

and a _____ . When he got there, he saw a

_____ and a _____ . When he got

back home, he was glad to see his _____ .

More Fun. On another sheet of paper, rewrite the story using different
words in the blank spaces. Draw a picture and then read your new story.

Read each **short a** word. Print the word and add **e**.
Read the new **long A** words.

c a n
1 2 3

cane
_____

m a n
4 2 3

_____

a t
2 5

_____

m a d
4 2 6

_____

p l a n
7 8 2 3

_____

p a s t
7 2 9 5

_____

A number is below each letter. Print the letters that go with the numbers on the lines below to read the message.

S__ __   w__ __   __ __ __
 2 4   2 9   4   2   6

w h e__   __ h e   __ __ __ __ e
    3   5   7 8 2 3

w__ __   __ __ __ e.
 2 9   8 2 5

hay

tail

pail

Words with **ay** and **ai** also make the **long A** sound.
Print the **long A** words. Read the words.

___**a y**___

h_____

tr_____

cl_____

st_____

pl_____

s_____

___**a i**___

p_____l

m_____l

tr_____n

t_____l

p_____nt

r_____n

Use the **long A** words to answer the riddles.

1. I ride on a track and travel from place to place.

    What am I? _____

2. I fall from the sky and water plants. What am I? _____

3. Farm animals eat me. What am I? _____

4. I am used to carry things. What am I? _____

5. I am at the end of a dog. What am I? _____

6. I am something you can do at recess. What am I? _____

All the words in the box have the **long E** sound. Read the **long E** words. Print each word in the puzzle where it fits.

funny   she
silly   we
happy   me
he   belly

Write a story about the clown using some of the **long E** words.

_____

_____

_____

_____

Sometimes **ee** and **ea** make the **long E** sound. Follow the path of **long E** words to get the deer to the stream.

More Fun. Now you know more **long E** words. On another sheet of paper, write a story using more new words. Draw a picture, and then read your new story.

Add **e** to the end of these words to change the **short i** to a **long I** sound. Read the words.

kit____ fir____ slid____ pin____

bit____ dim____ rip____ rid____

Use **short i** and **long I** words to finish the story.

Tim _____ down the _____ . He got a

_____ in his pants. Then he bought a _____

for only a _____ . The _____ got stuck in

a _____ tree. What a time Tim had today!

Sometimes **y**, **ie**, and **igh** make the **long I** sound.
Add and subtract letters to write **long I** words. Read the words.

pie

cry

th+ry-h = _____try_____   t+ib+he-bh = _____

w+sh-s+y = _____   li+gr+ht-r = _____

ch+re-he+y = _____   n+igh+wt-w = _____

p+li+ed-ld = _____   hi+gs+h-s = _____

Add **o** and **e** to make **long O** words.
Read the words.

phone

rose

note

b <u>o</u> n <u>e</u>   h __ s __   m __ l __

ph __ n __   r __ s __   n __ t __

h __ m __   j __ k __   st __ n __

r __ p __   c __ n __   st __ v __

Use the words above to solve the puzzle.

Across

3. rock
4. where you live
6. flower

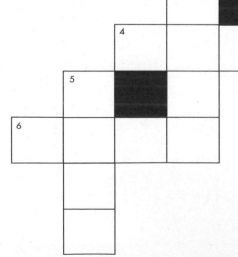

Down

1. short letter
2. used to tie something
3. used for cooking
5. funny riddle

The letters **oa** make the **long O** sound. Use the **long O** words below to complete the story.

boat	coat	toast
float	toad	oak
goat	coast	road

A _____ wanted to _____ in a

_____ up the _____ . He met a

_____ wearing a _____ hopping down

the _____ . "Come to my house by the

_____ tree and we will have tea and _____,"

said the _____ . So he did.

Long U

Add **u** and **e** to make **long U** words.

m __ l __   t __ b __

fl __ t __   h __ g __

c __ b __   r __ l __

c __ t __   t __ n __

__ s __   J __ n __

mule

Color all the **long U** words to find something that makes music.

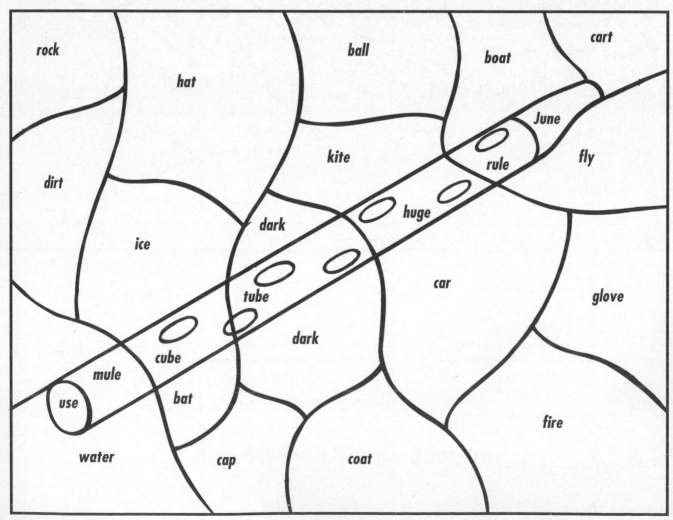

The letters **ue** and **ui** often make the **long U** sound.
Use the **long U** words in the box to solve the riddles.

blue   glue   fruit   suit   juice

1. I am a color. What am I? _____

2. I am used to stick things together. What am I? _____

3. I am not a vegetable. I am a _____.

4. I am something you wear for swimming. What am I? _____

5. I am a drink made from fruit. What am I?_____

clown

flag

flower

Print the **l blends** to make new words.

bl	cl	fl
___ock	___ay	___y
___anket	___ock	___ower
___ack	___own	___ag

gl	pl	sl
___ue	___ate	___ide
___ove	___um	___eep
___obe	___ay	___ed

Print the words to answer the riddles.

1. I cover you at night.

2. I tell the time.

3. I fly on the pole.

4. I cover your hand.

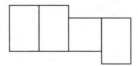

5. I am a purple fruit.

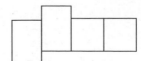

6. I slide down hills fast.

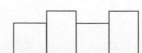

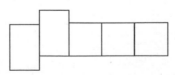

Look up, down, across, and diagonally for the **r blend** words. Circle the words.

crown

frog

drum

broom	crown	frog	drum	pretty
brush	crab	fruit	dress	prize
brick	crib	friend	drink	present

a b r o o m d a n f m s d d

g r d c s q r c b r i c k r

h u i o o k i m h i f b c e

f r o g a w n v p e h r d s

t r m a o q k c n n u u m s

s i u w f r l e h d r s s y

z t p i b n q h i e n h v n

a y t b t w z s v k l p b o

d r u m k o u r y t t e r p

t h e z i r p r e s e n t v

v d b i r c a w g m c r a b

More Fun. Write a story using your new words. Draw a picture.

Add and subtract letters to write **st**, **sp**, and **sn** words.
Read the words.

st + amy + p - y = _____

sp + loo - l + n = _____

sn + aie + l - e = _____

s + ta + dr - d = _____

s + pid + ler -l = _____

sn + ack + e - c = _____

Use long vowel rhyming families to make new words.

ay	ide	old
pl _____	r _____	b _____
st _____	h _____	c _____
d _____	s _____	g _____
s _____	sl _____	s _____
cl _____	gl _____	t _____

Use your new words to make up a silly story. Read your story.

One _____, Jay wanted to _____ outside.

He went to _____ down the hill on his sled. The

weather was so _____ he did not _____

long. His mother _____ him to come in and play

with _____. What do you think Jay would _____?

Contractions

Some words can be put together by replacing letters with an apostrophe. Draw lines to match the words and **contractions**.

would not   I've
do not   couldn't
could not   didn't
did not   that's
I am   wouldn't
had not   don't
that is   hadn't
I have   I'm

Use the **contractions** to finish the story. Answers may vary.

"I _____ do that if I were you," warned Mom. She

knew I _____ have time to play outside because

I _____ finished my homework. "_____

planning to finish my homework when it gets dark," I said.

"I _____ have much left to do." "_____

not the first time _____ heard that excuse," said Mom.

Sometimes two letters together make a new sound. Look at the pictures and read the words.

chair

cheese

chicken

ship

sheep

shovel

elephant

dolphin

whistle

Use the words to solve the puzzle.

Across

1. a referee uses this
3. food made from milk
5. sea mammal

Down

2. animal with a thick coat
4. large boat

CHALLENGE

Write in missing letters to form these words:

E L E P H _ N _

_ E L E P H _ N _

Compound Words

When you put two words together to make a new word, you make a **compound word**. Draw lines to make new words.

fly   cow   cup   box   rain

foot   fire   star   mail

tooth   ball   cake   bell

boy   fish   brush   bow

Print the new words on the lines.
How many words can you make?

_____

_____

_____

_____

You can use **ir**, **er**, and **ur** to spell the same sound. Look at the pictures and read the words.

nurse   bird   farmer   girl

dinner   shirt   purse   turtle

Unscramble the letters to write **ir**, **er**, and **ur** words.

nsrue _____   lirg _____

rdbi _____   sruep _____

hrsit _____   trlteu _____

marfer _____   nidren _____

Plural means more than one. Look at the pictures and print the plural words. Add **s** to the following words.

 clock _____

flower _____

 dog _____

When the word ends in **x**, **ss**, **ch**, or **sh**, add **es**.

box _____

 dress _____

dish _____

 peach _____

Usually, when the word ends in **y**, you change the **y** to **i** and add **es**.

baby _____

 butterfly _____

When added to the beginning of a word, **re** means "again," **in** means "not," **un** means "not," and **dis** can mean "not." Add the word parts together. Read the words.

un + happy = _____   dis + agree = _____

un + safe = _____   re + work = _____

re + build = _____   dis + like = _____

in + correct = _____

Look up, down, across, and diagonally to find the **prefix** words in the puzzle. Circle the words.

d u b t g j q m p l a
i n c o r r e c t z b
s h m j k e t w a n o
a a b u g w b x b w n
g p t u c o y u z v f
r p q u d r m p i s p
e y r n b k t u m l x
e d i s l i k e f n d
x y l a b d g h w o r
p n m f c a m t v p m
q s v e h q r b d i p

Suffixes: ful, ly, less

When added to the end of a word, **ful** means "full of," **ly** turns the word into a "how" word, and **less** means "without." Add the word parts together. Read the words. Use the words to solve the puzzle.

help + ful =_____   home + less =_____

neat + ly =_____   end + less =_____

soft + ly =_____   thank + ful =_____

use + less =_____   care + less =_____

care + ful =_____

Read the clues. Use the **suffix** words to solve the puzzle.

Across
1. not careful
3. to be of help
4. orderly
5. no use for

Down
2. quietly
3. without a home

Page 1

Consonants

The consonants are b, c, d, f, g, h, j, k, l, m, n, p, q, r, s, t, v, w, x, y, z.
Say the name of each picture.
Print the missing **consonants** to finish each word. Read the words.

d o g
p a i l
b a t
c a r
h a t
j a r
f o x
y a k
q u a i l
v i o l i n
w a g o n
z e b r a

There is a number below each letter you printed. To read the message, fill in each blank with the letter that goes with the number.

I l i k e t o s p e l l

DISCOVERY WORKBOOK 1 PHONICS II

Page 2

Short a

Short a is the sound you hear at the beginning of the word ant.

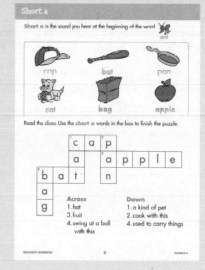

cap bat pan
cat bag apple

Read the clues. Use the **short a** words in the box to finish the puzzle.

c a p
a a p p l e
b a t n
a
g

Across
1. hat
3. fruit
4. swing at a ball with this

Down
1. a kind of pet
2. cook with this
4. used to carry things

DISCOVERY WORKBOOK 2 PHONICS II

Page 3

Short e

Short e is the sound you hear at the beginning of the word egg.
Print e to make **short e** words. Read the words.

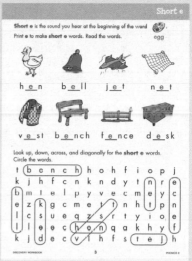

h e n b e l l j e t n e t
v e s t b e n c h f e n c e d e s k

Look up, down, across, and diagonally for the **short e** words. Circle the words.

t b e n c h h o h f i o p j
k j h f c n k n d y t n r c
b m l e l p y v e m h e t p
e z k g c m e t t n h h t o
l c s u e q z s r t y i o e
l e e c h e n q a k h y f
k j d e c v l h f s t e j h

DISCOVERY WORKBOOK 3 PHONICS II

Page 4

Short i

Short i is the sound you hear at the beginning of the word igloo.
Use the **short i** words in the box to answer the riddles.

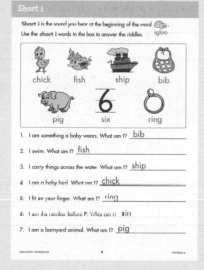

chick fish ship bib
pig six ring

1. I am something a baby wears. What am I? bib
2. I swim. What am I? fish
3. I carry things across the water. What am I? ship
4. I am a baby bird. What am I? chick
5. I fit on your finger. What am I? ring
6. I am the number before 7. What am I? six
7. I am a barnyard animal. What am I? pig

DISCOVERY WORKBOOK 4 PHONICS II

Page 5

Short o

Short o is the sound you hear at the beginning of the word octopus.
Use the **short o** words to create a story.

pond log hop rock frog got fox

The fox jumped over a log near a small pond. She saw a frog hiding behind a large rock. With a hop the frog got to the pond.

Draw a picture of your story.

More Fun. On another sheet of paper, rewrite the story using different words in the blank spaces. Draw a picture and then read your new story.

DISCOVERY WORKBOOK 5 PHONICS II

Page 6

Short u

Short u is the sound you hear at the beginning of the word umbrella.
Color the spaces with the **short u** words to find the answer to the riddle below.

Everyone "nose" me! What am I? _____

DISCOVERY WORKBOOK 6 PHONICS II

Page 7

Rhyming Families at, ed, ing, ock, and ug

Use short vowel rhyming families to make new words.

at	ed	ing	ock	ug
b at	bed	king	clock	b ug
cat	fed	ring	dock	dug
fat	led	sing	lock	hug
hat	red	swing	sock	rug
sat	sled	wing	rock	tug

Use your new words to make up a silly story. Read your story.
Answers may vary.

One day a king went on a trip. He packed a bat, a hat, a sock, and a rock. When he got there, he saw a swing and a clock. When he got back home, he was glad to see his cat.

More Fun. On another sheet of paper, rewrite the story using different words in the blank spaces. Draw a picture and then read your new story.

DISCOVERY WORKBOOK 7 PHONICS II

Page 8

Long A

Read each **short a** word. Print the word and add e.
Read the new **long A** words.

can → cane
1 2 3
man → mane
4 2 3
at → ate
2 5
mad → made
4 2 6
plan → plane
1 8 2 3
past → paste
7 9 5

A number is below each letter. Print the letters that go with the numbers on the lines below to read the message.

S u m w u s m a d
2 4 3 6
w h e n t h e p l a n e
8 3 1 8 2 3
w a s l a t e.
2 9 8 2 5

DISCOVERY WORKBOOK 8 PHONICS II

Page 9

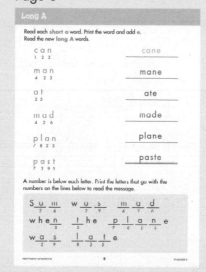

Words with **ay** and **ai** also make the **long A** sound.
Print the **long A** words. Read the words.

ay	ai
h ay	p ai l
tr ay	m ai l
cl ay	tr ai n
st ay	t ai l
pl ay	p ai nt
s ay	r ai n

Use the **long A** words to answer the riddles.
1. I ride on a track and travel from place to place. What am I? train
2. I fall from the sky and water plants. What am I? rain
3. Farm animals eat me. What am I? hay
4. I am used to carry things. What am I? pail/tray
5. I am at the end of a dog. What am I? tail
6. I am something you can do at recess. What am I? play

DISCOVERY WORKBOOK 9 PHONICS II

Answers

Page 10

Long E

All the words in the box have the **long E** sound. Read the **long E** words. Print each word in the puzzle where it fits.

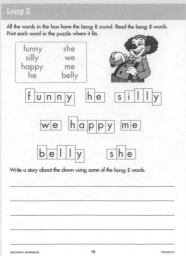

funny	she
silly	we
happy	me
he	belly

f u n n y   h e   s i l l y

w e   h a p p y   m e

b e l l y   s h e

Write a story about the clown using some of the long E words.

_____

_____

_____

_____

_____

Page 11

Sometimes **ee** and **ea** make the **long E** sound. Follow the path of long E words to get the deer to the stream.

More Fun. Now you know more **long E** words. On another sheet of paper, write a story using more new words. Draw a picture, and then read your new story.

Page 12

Long I

Add **e** to the end of these words to change the **short i** to a **long I** sound. Read the words.

kit_e_   fir_e_   slid_e_   pin_e_

bit_e_   dim_e_   rip_e_   rid_e_

Use **short i** and **long I** words to finish the story.

Tim __slid__ down the __slide__ . He got a

__rip__ in his pants. Then he bought a __kite__

for only a __dime__ . The __kite__ got stuck in

a __pine/fir__ tree. What a time Tim had today!

Page 13

Sometimes **y**, **ie**, and **igh** make the **long I** sound. Add and subtract letters to write **long I** words. Read the words.

th+ry-h= __try__   t+ib+he-bh= __tie__

w+sh-s+y= __why__   li+gr+ht-r= __light__

ch+re-he+y= __cry__   n+igh+wt-w= __night__

p+li+ed-ld= __pie__   hi+gs+h-s= __high__

Page 14

Long O

Add **o** and **e** to make **long O** words. Read the words.

b_o_n_e_   h_o_s_e_   m_o_l_e_
ph_o_n_e_   r_o_s_e_   n_o_t_e_
h_o_m_e_   j_o_k_e_   st_o_n_e_
r_o_p_e_   c_o_n_e_   st_o_v_e_

Use the words above to solve the puzzle.

Across
3. rock
4. where you live
6. flower

Down
1. short letter
2. used to tie something
3. used for cooking
5. funny riddle

Page 15

The letters **oa** make the **long O** sound. Use the **long O** words below to complete the story.

boat	coat	toast
float	toad	oak
goat	coast	road

A __goat__ wanted to __float__ in a

__boat__ up the __coast__ . He met a

__toad__ wearing a __coat__ hopping down

the __road__ . "Come to my house by the

__oak__ tree and we will have tea and __toast__ ,"

said the __toad/goat__ . So he did.

Page 16

Long U

Add **u** and **e** to make **long U** words.

m_u_l_e_   t_u_b_e_
fl_u_t_e_   h_u_g_e_
c_u_b_e_   r_u_l_e_
c_u_t_e_   t_u_n_e_
_u_s_e_   J_u_n_e_

Color all the **long U** words to find something that makes music.

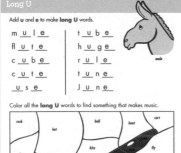

Page 17

The letters **ue** and **ui** often make the **long U** sound. Use the **long U** words in the box to solve the riddles.

blue   glue   fruit   suit   juice

1. I am a color. What am I? __blue__

2. I am used to stick things together. What am I? __glue__

3. I am not a vegetable. I am a __fruit__

4. I am something you wear for swimming. What am I? __suit__

5. I am a drink made from fruit. What am I? __juice__

Page 18

l blends

Print the **l blends** to make new words.

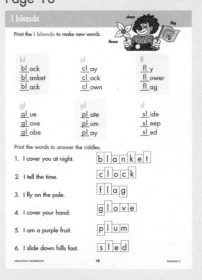

bl   cl   fl
bl_ock_   cl_ay_   fl_y_
bl_anket_   cl_ock_   fl_ower_
bl_ack_   cl_own_   fl_ag_

gl   pl   sl
gl_ue_   pl_ate_   sl_ide_
gl_ove_   pl_um_   sl_eep_
gl_obe_   pl_ay_   sl_ed_

Print the words to answer the riddles.

1. I cover you at night.   b l a n k e t

2. I tell the time.   c l o c k

3. I fly on the pole.   f l a g

4. I cover your hand.   g l o v e

5. I am a purple fruit.   p l u m

6. I slide down hills fast.   s l e d

Answers

Page 19

r blends

Look up, down, across, and diagonally for the r blend words. Circle the words.

broom	crown	frog	drum	pretty
brush	crab	fruit	dress	prize
brick	crib	friend	drink	present

```
a  b  r  o  o  m  d  a  n  f  m  s  d  d
g  r  d  c  s  q  r  c  b  r  i  c  k  e
h  u  i  o  o  k  i  m  h  i  f  b  c  e
f  r  o  g  a  w  n  v  p  e  h  r  b  s
t  r  m  a  o  q  k  c  n  n  u  r  u  m
s  i  u  w  f  r  l  e  h  d  r  s  s  y
z  t  p  i  b  n  q  h  i  e  n  h  h  v  n
a  y  t  b  t  w  z  s  v  k  l  p  b  o
d  r  u  m  k  o  u  r  y  t  t  e  r  p
t  h  e  z  i  r  p  r  e  s  e  n  t  v
v  d  b  i  r  c  a  w  g  m  c  r  a  b
```

More Fun. Write a story using your new words. Draw a picture.

DISCOVERY WORKBOOK   19   PHONICS 5

Page 20

st, sp, and sn blends

Add and subtract letters to write st, sp, and sn words. Read the words.

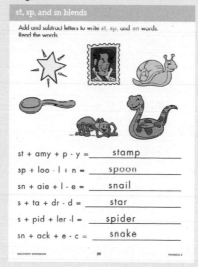

st + amy + p - y = __stamp__

sp + loo - l + n = __spoon__

sn + aie + l - e = __snail__

s + ta + dr - d = __star__

s + pid + ler -l = __spider__

sn + ack + e - c = __snake__

DISCOVERY WORKBOOK   20   PHONICS 5

Page 21

Rhyming Families: ay, ide, old

Use long vowel rhyming families to make new words.

ay	ide	old
pl __ay__	r __ide__	b __old__
st __ay__	h __ide__	c __old__
d __ay__	s __ide__	g __old__
s __ay__	sl __ide__	s __old__
cl __ay__	gl __ide__	t __old__

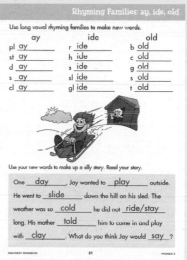

Use your new words to make up a silly story. Read your story.

One __day__, Jay wanted to __play__ outside.

He went to __slide__ down the hill on his sled. The

weather was so __cold__ he did not __ride/stay__

long. His mother __told__ him to come in and play

with __clay__. What do you think Jay would __say__?

DISCOVERY WORKBOOK   21   PHONICS 5

Page 22

Contractions

Some words can be put together by replacing letters with an apostrophe. Draw lines to match the words and **contractions**.

would not — I've
do not — couldn't
could not — didn't
did not — that's
I am — wouldn't
had not — don't
that is — hadn't
I have — I'm

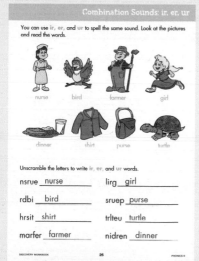

Use the **contractions** to finish the story. Answers may vary.

"I __wouldn't__ do that if I were you," warned Mom. She

knew I __didn't__ have time to play outside because

I __hadn't__ finished my homework. "I'm __I'm__

planning to finish my homework when it gets dark," I said.

"I __don't__ have much left to do." "That's __That's__

not the first time I've __I've__ heard that excuse," said Mom.

DISCOVERY WORKBOOK   22   PHONICS 5

Page 23

Combination Sounds: ch, sh, ph, wh

Sometimes two letters together make a new sound. Look at the pictures and read the words.

chair   cheese   chicken   ship   sheep
shovel   elephant   dolphin   whistle

Use the words to solve the puzzle.

Across
1. a referee uses this
3. food made from milk
5. sea mammal

Down
2. animal with a thick coat
4. large boat

```
w h i s t l e
    h
c h e e s e
    e     h
d o l p h i n
    p
```

CHALLENGE
Write in missing letters to form these words:

ELEPH__ANT__
T__ELEPHONE__

DISCOVERY WORKBOOK   23   PHONICS 5

Page 24

Compound Words

When you put two words together to make a new word, you make a **compound word**. Draw lines to make new words.

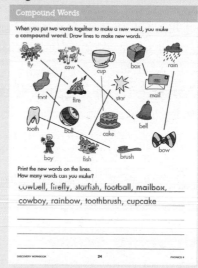

fly   cow   cup   box   rain
front   fire   star   mail
tooth   ball   cake   bell
boy   fish   brush   bow

Print the new words on the lines. How many words can you make?

cowbell, firefly, starfish, football, mailbox,

cowboy, rainbow, toothbrush, cupcake

DISCOVERY WORKBOOK   24   PHONICS 5

Page 25

Combination Sounds: ir, er, ur

You can use ir, er, and ur to spell the same sound. Look at the pictures and read the words.

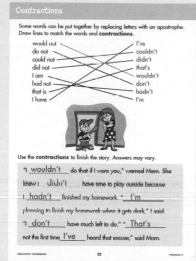

nurse   bird   farmer   girl
dinner   shirt   purse   turtle

Unscramble the letters to write ir, er, and ur words.

nsrue __nurse__   lirg __girl__

rdbi __bird__   sruep __purse__

hrsit __shirt__   trlteu __turtle__

marfer __farmer__   nidren __dinner__

DISCOVERY WORKBOOK   25   PHONICS 5

Page 26

More Than One

Plural means more than one. Look at the pictures and print the plural words. Add s to the following words.

clock — __clocks__

flower — __flowers__

dog — __dogs__

When the word ends in x, ss, ch, or sh, add es.

box — __boxes__

dress — __dresses__

dish — __dishes__

peach — __peaches__

Usually, when the word ends in y, you change the y to i and add es.

baby — __babies__

butterfly — __butterflies__

DISCOVERY WORKBOOK   26   PHONICS 5

Page 27

Prefixes: re, in, un, dis

When added to the beginning of a word, **re** means "again," **in** means "not," **un** means "not," and **dis** can mean "not." Add the word parts together. Read the words.

un + happy = __unhappy__   dis + agree = __disagree__

un + safe = __unsafe__   re + work = __rework__

re + build = __rebuild__   dis + like = __dislike__

in + correct = __incorrect__

Look up, down, across, and diagonally to find the **prefix** words in the puzzle. Circle the words.

```
d  u  b  t  g  j  q  m  p  l  a
i  n  c  o  r  r  e  c  t  z  b
s  h  m  j  k  e  t  w  a  n  o
a  a  b  u  g  w  b  x  b  w  n
g  p  t  u  c  o  y  u  z  v  f
r  q  q  u  n  r  m  p  i  o  u
e  q  n  b  k  r  t  u  n  l  x
e  d  i  s  l  i  k  e  f  n  d
x  y  l  a  b  d  g  h  w  o  r
p  n  m  f  c  a  m  t  v  p  m
q  s  v  e  h  q  r  b  d  i  p
```

DISCOVERY WORKBOOK   27   PHONICS 5

Family Fun Activities

The following activities will provide additional review of the concepts explored on the workbook pages.

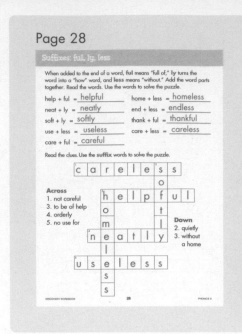

1. Vowel Game

Play a vowel game. Name an object in the room. Ask your child to name another object with the same vowel sound or sounds. For example, pie and ice cream both have a long "I" sound.

2. Beginning Sounds

Create a book with 21 blank pages. Write one consonant on each page. (The consonants are listed on page 1 of the workbook.) Help your child cut out pictures from magazines and glue them on the page whose consonant begins the picture word. For additional review, ask your child to name each letter and say the sound or sounds associated with it. Encourage the child to continue adding pictures to the book.

3. Compound Word Game

Write compound words on index cards. Write one word on each card. (For compound word suggestions use the answer page for page 24 of the workbook.) Cut each index card so the individual words are separated. Mix up the cards. Ask your child to reassemble and read the compound words. As your child learns more compound words, create more cards to add to the game.

4. Rhyming Game

Ask your child to create a list of rhyming words. Choose rhyming words that can be illustrated (i.e., bat and cat). On half-sized index cards, write each word. Suggest that the child illustrate the cards. Mix up the cards and place them upside-down on a table. Ask your child to try to turn over a rhyming pair. If the child guesses correctly, he or she keeps the pair and tries again. If the pairs do not rhyme, they are turned back over and play passes to the next player. The game ends when all pairs are matched. The player with the most matched rhyming pairs wins the game.

5. Story Writing

Encourage your child to apply newly-developed phonics skills to story writing. Use the "More Fun" activities at the bottom of the workbook pages to stimulate additional story writing. Ask your child to read you the story when it is completed. Read the story back to your child.